FAIRY TALE PHONICS

DAISY FLIES WITH A DRAGON
A TALE OF VOWEL SOUNDS

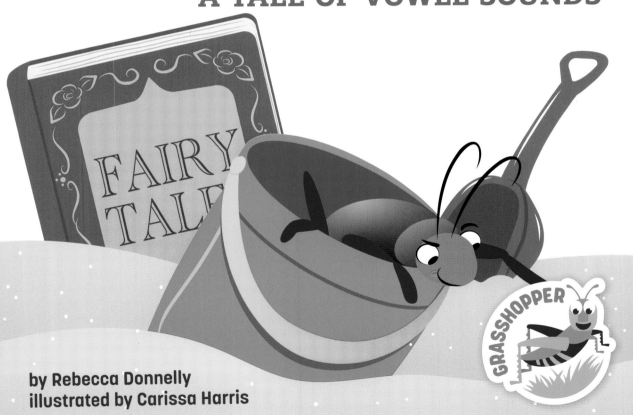

by Rebecca Donnelly
illustrated by Carissa Harris

GRASSHOPPER

Tools for Parents & Teachers

Grasshopper Books enhance imagination and introduce the earliest readers to fiction with fun storylines and illustrations. The easy-to-read text supports early reading experiences with repetitive sentence patterns and sight words.

Before Reading

• Discuss the cover illustration. What do readers see?

• Look at the picture glossary together. Discuss the words.

Read the Book

• Read the book to the child, or have him or her read independently.

• "Walk" through the book and look at the illustrations. Who is the main character? What is happening in the story?

After Reading

• Prompt the child to think more. Ask: Look at the objects around you. Say the names of them aloud. Which ones have long vowel sounds? Which have short vowel sounds? How do you know?

Grasshopper Books are published by Jump!
5357 Penn Avenue South
Minneapolis, MN 55419
www.jumplibrary.com

Library of Congress Cataloging-in-Publication Data

Names: Donnelly, Rebecca, author. Harris, Carissa, illustrator.
Title: Daisy flies with a dragon: a tale of vowel sounds by Rebecca Donnelly; illustrated by Carissa Harris.
Description: Minneapolis, MN: Jump!, Inc., [2023]
Series: Fairy tale phonics | Includes index.
Audience: Ages 5-8
Identifiers: LCCN 2022030319 (print)
LCCN 2022030320 (ebook)
ISBN 9798885242691 (hardcover)
ISBN 9798885242707 (paperback)
ISBN 9798885242714 (ebook)
Subjects: LCSH: Readers (Primary) | Dragons–Juvenile fiction.
LCGFT: Readers (Publications)
Classification: LCC PE1119.2 .D673 2023 (print)
LCC PE1119.2 (ebook)
DDC 428.6/2–dc23/eng/20220629
LC record available at https://lccn.loc.gov/2022030319
LC ebook record available at https://lccn.loc.gov/2022030320

Editor: Eliza Leahy
Direction and Layout: Anna Peterson
Illustrator: Carissa Harris

Printed in the United States of America at Corporate Graphics in North Mankato, Minnesota.

Table of Contents

In This Book:

You will find long and short vowel sounds. A long vowel makes the sound of the letter's name, like the a in cave. A short vowel does not make the sound of the letter's name, like the a in badger. Can you find long and short vowels on each page?

Fly High in the Sky

Daisy hikes up a mountain.

She finds a cave!

She hears a voice coming from inside.

It is a dragon!

"Hi! I'm Drake," says the dragon.

"I'm Daisy. What are you reading?" asks Daisy.

"Fairy tales," says Drake. "But they are not easy to read. Do you know vowel sounds?"

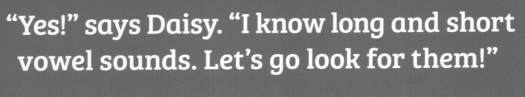

"Yes!" says Daisy. "I know long and short vowel sounds. Let's go look for them!"

"Hop on my back!" says Drake. "We will fly high in the sky!"

"Hold on!" says Drake.

"Long vowels make the same sound as their names," says Daisy. "Like the *a* in lake!"

"Yay!" says Drake.

"Look, a badger! Badger has a short *a* sound," says Daisy.

"That badger has a black hat!" says Drake.

"What has a long *e*?" asks Daisy.

"A beach!" says Drake.
"And green leaves on trees."

"And a short *e*?" asks Daisy.

"A red hen that is about
to get wet!" Drake says.

hen

"I spy an icy island!" Daisy says.

"That is a long *i*," says Drake.

"Right!" says Daisy.

"A gingerbread kid!" says Daisy in surprise.

"It is in a little ship," says Drake.

"A dune!" says Daisy.

"Uh-oh!" says Drake. "A bug is stuck in a bucket."

dune

"What has a long *o* sound?" asks Daisy.

"I see a lot of frogs on a rock," says Drake. "But those are short *o* sounds."

"I know!" says Drake. "Let's go home."

"Thank you for helping me!" says Drake. "Can we learn more letter sounds soon?"

"Oh yes, I hope so!" says Daisy.

Let's Review!

Long vowels, like the **a** in l**a**ke, make the same sound as their name. Short vowels, like the **e** in h**e**n, do not. Which words below have long vowel sounds? Which have short vowel sounds?

ship

icy

hen

dune

bucket

hat

lake

beach

rock

Picture Glossary

cave
A large opening underground, in a hillside, or in a cliff.

dragon
An imaginary monster that can fly and breathe fire.

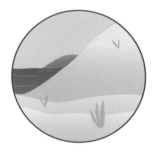

dune
A sand hill formed by wind or tides.

fairy tales
Children's stories about magical beings such as fairies, giants, and witches.

gingerbread
A brown cake or cookie flavored with ginger and other spices.

island
A piece of land surrounded by water.

Index

To Learn More

FACT SURFER

Finding more information is as easy as 1, 2, 3.

❶ Go to www.factsurfer.com

❷ Enter "**Daisyflieswithadragon**" into the search box.

❸ Choose your book to see a list of websites.